A Note to Parents

DK READERS is a compelling programme for beginning readers, designed in conjunction with leading literacy experts, including Maureen Fernandes. B.Ed (hons). Maureen has spent many years teaching literacy, both in the classroom and as a consultant in schools.

Beautiful illustrations and superb full-colour photographs combine with engaging, easy-to-read stories to offer a fresh approach to each subject in the series. Each DK READER is guaranteed to capture a child's interest while developing his or her reading skills, general knowledge and love of reading.

The five levels of DK READERS are aimed at different reading abilities, enabling you to choose the books that are exactly right for your child:

Pre-level 1: Learning to read
Level 1: Beginning to read
Level 2: Beginning to read alone
Level 3: Reading alone
Level 4: Proficient readers

The "normal" age at which a child begins to read can be anywhere from three to eight years old. Adult participation through the lower levels is very helpful for providing encouragement, discussing storylines, and sounding out unfamiliar words.

No matter which level you select, you can be sure that you are helping your child learn to read, then read to learn!

LONDON, NEW YORK, MUNICH,
MELBOURNE, AND DELHI

For Dorling Kindersley
Managing Art Editor Ron Stobbart
Publishing Manager Catherine Saunders
Art Director Lisa Lanzarini
Publisher Simon Beecroft
Publishing Director Alex Allan
Production Editor Marc Staples
Production Controller Kara Wallace
Reading Consultant Maureen Fernandes

For Lucasfilm
Executive Editor J. W. Rinzler
Art Director Troy Alders
Keeper of the Holocron Leland Chee
Director of Publishing Carol Roeder

Designed and edited by Tall Tree Ltd
Designer Ben Ruocco
Editor Jon Richards

Acknowledgements
The author would like to thank Linus Beecroft
for his help on this book.

First published in Great Britain in 2012 by
Dorling Kindersley Limited
80 Strand, London WC2R 0RL

12 13 14 15 16 10 9 8 7 6 5 4 3 2 1

001–182941–05/12

A CIP catalogue record for this book
is available from the British Library

ISBN: 9781409383192

Printed and bound in China by L. Rex Printing Company Ltd

Discover more at
www.dk.com
www.starwars.com

DK READERS

BEGINNING 2 TO READ ALONE

STAR WARS™

THE CLONE WARS™

Chewbacca and the Wookiee Warriors

Written by
Simon Beecroft

Have you met Chewbacca?
Chewbacca is a Wookiee.
He comes from a planet
called Kashyyyk.
He is tall and strong and his
body is covered with hair.

Wookiee words

Chewbacca can understand our words.
But he can't speak them, because his
mouth cannot make the sounds.
He can only speak the Wookiee language.

When he
speaks,
Chewbacca
shows his
sharp teeth
and growls!

It is not a good idea to upset Chewbacca. He might try to pull your arm off!

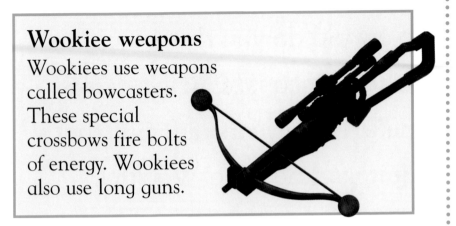

Wookiee weapons
Wookiees use weapons called bowcasters. These special crossbows fire bolts of energy. Wookiees also use long guns.

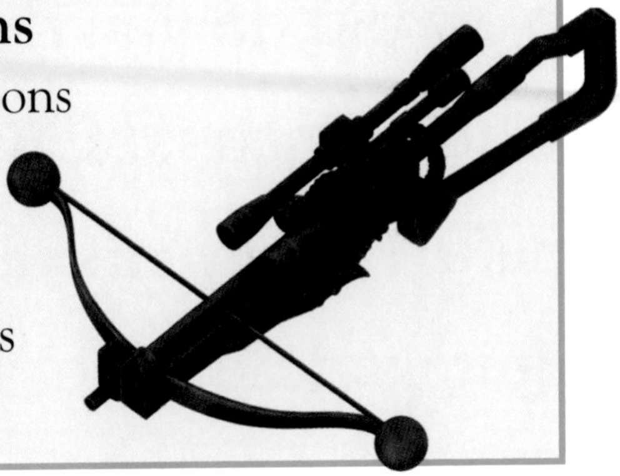

Chewbacca trained as a warrior. He has a ferocious temper and great strength. But he is usually friendly.

Wookiees are very intelligent. They build cities in the tall trees on their planet. They fly starships through space. They are also really good at fixing spaceship engines.

How old do you think Chewbacca is? Chewbacca is nearly 200 years old! But that's quite young for a Wookiee. Wookiees can live for more than 600 years.

Jedi student

Ahsoka Tano is a Jedi student, called a Padawan. The Jedi are warrior monks who use a mysterious energy called the Force to increase their powers.

Look at how much taller Chewbacca is than Ahsoka!

Fully grown Wookiees are much taller than most humans.

Tarfful is Chewbacca's friend.
He is a Wookiee chieftain.
He and Chewbacca have fought side-by-side in many battles.

During the Clone Wars, Tarfful and Chewbacca defended their world from a deadly droid army. Like Chewbacca, Tarfful is calm and thoughtful. But in battle, he is ferocious!

The Clone Wars

The Clone Wars were a huge conflict in the galaxy. Deadly droid armies invaded many worlds and tried to take them over by force.

Trandoshans are the Wookiees' deadly enemies. Trandoshans are large reptiles and their skin is covered in scales. Their hands and feet have three razor-sharp claws.

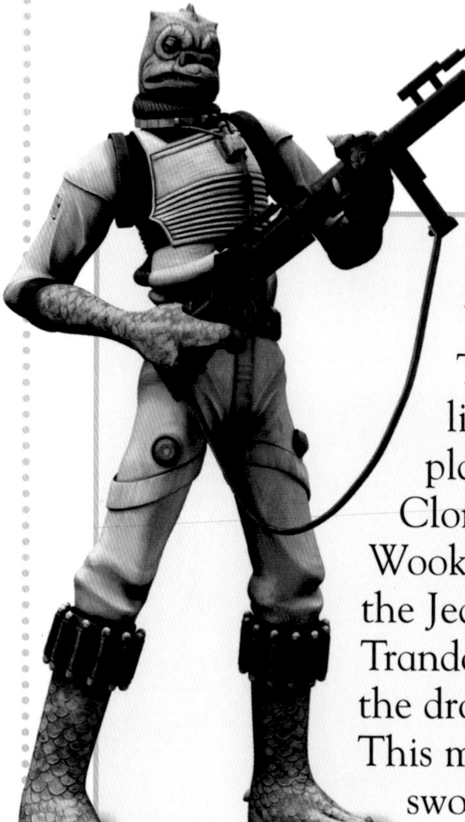

Old enemies

Wookiees and Trandoshans live on nearby planets. In the Clone Wars, the Wookiees support the Jedi and the Trandoshans support the droid armies. This makes them sworn enemies.

Trandoshans are warlike and dangerous. They like to hunt and capture Wookiees for fun.

Trandoshan hunters release captured Wookiees and other species on an isolated forest moon called Wasskah. Then they hunt the captives on the moon, just for fun.

Hunting Speeders

Trandoshan hunters use hunting speeders to chase after their prey. The speeders are armed with powerful cannons.

Once, some Trandoshans captured a group of Padawans, including Ahsoka. They took them to Wasskah. Ahsoka hides from the Trandoshans under a tree. Can you spot her?

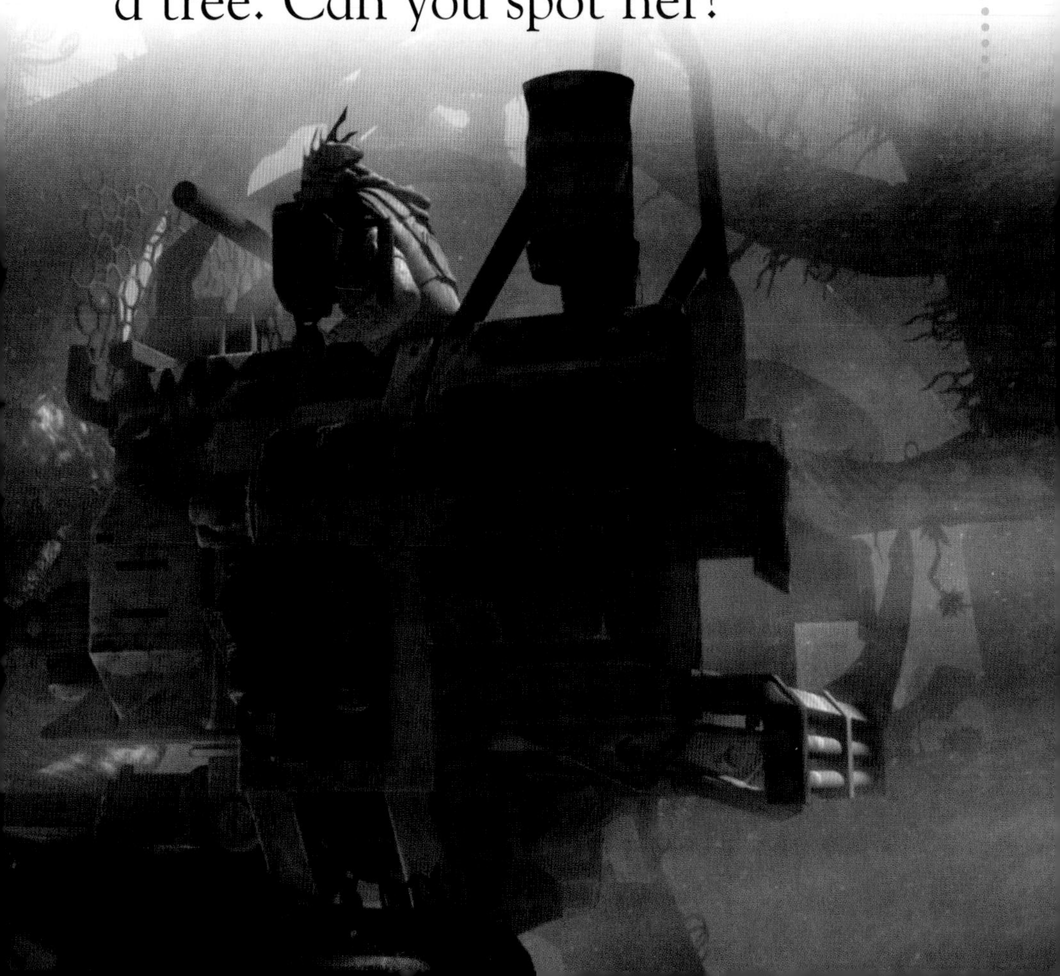

Ahsoka and the Padawans spot a Trandoshan spaceship.

They leap onto the top of the spaceship before it lands. They battle their way inside the spaceship.

Ahsoka surprises the pilot with a flying Jedi kick! But watch out! Now no one is steering the ship...

The Jedi leap from the ship just before it crashes. The ship also has a prisoner, locked up in a cage. When the ship crashes, the cage opens, and the prisoner walks free. It is Chewbacca!

Ahsoka and Chewbacca realise they can help each other. Chewbacca tries to mend the crashed ship's transmitter to call for help. But he cannot get it to work.

The Jedi Padawans have an idea. They capture a Trandoshan hunter and use their powers to control his mind. They tell him to call the other Trandoshans and ask to be picked up.

A hunting speeder appears. Our heroes hide until the speeder reaches the mind-tricked Trandoshan.

When the speeder is close,
Ahsoka leaps high in the air
and kicks out the pilot.
She then jumps out after him.
On the ground, the pilot gets
up to fight Ahsoka.

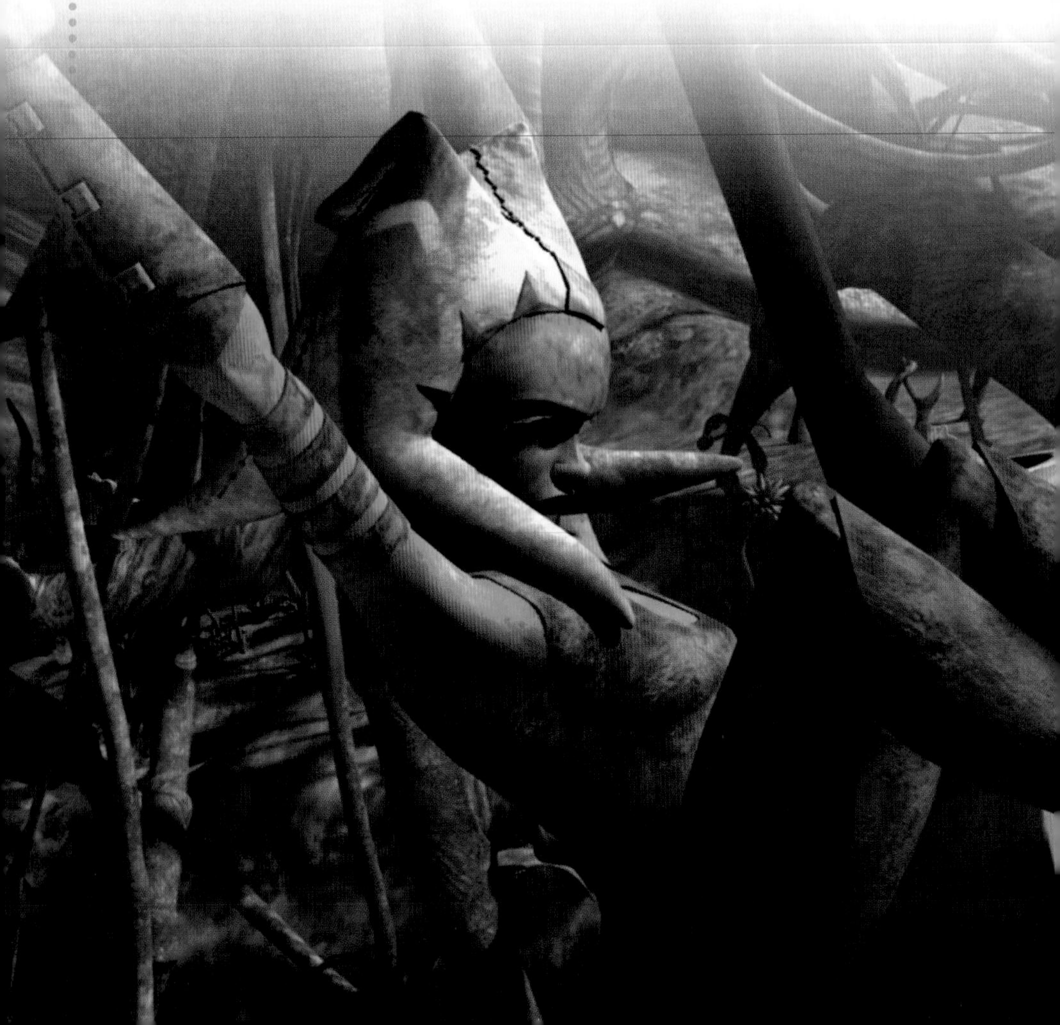

He thinks she looks easy to beat.

But he's wrong...

Ahsoka is a well-trained Jedi. She also has a Wookiee for a friend! Now it is the pilot who looks up, because Chewbacca is so tall. The pilot is not so sure of himself now!

Chewbacca bashes the pilot. One bash from Chewbacca is enough to knock out the pilot! Chewbacca and the Jedi fly off in the Trandoshan speeder. It's time to escape this moon!

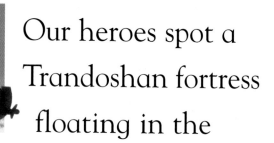

Our heroes spot a Trandoshan fortress floating in the clouds. The Trandoshan guards are surprised to see a hunting speeder arrive with a Wookiee and three Jedi on board!

Floating fortress

The Trandoshan hunters' base is a floating fortress. Inside, the Trandoshans display the creatures they have hunted.

Chewbacca and the Jedi fight the guards. Suddenly, one of the guards makes a loud screeching noise. He is calling for help.

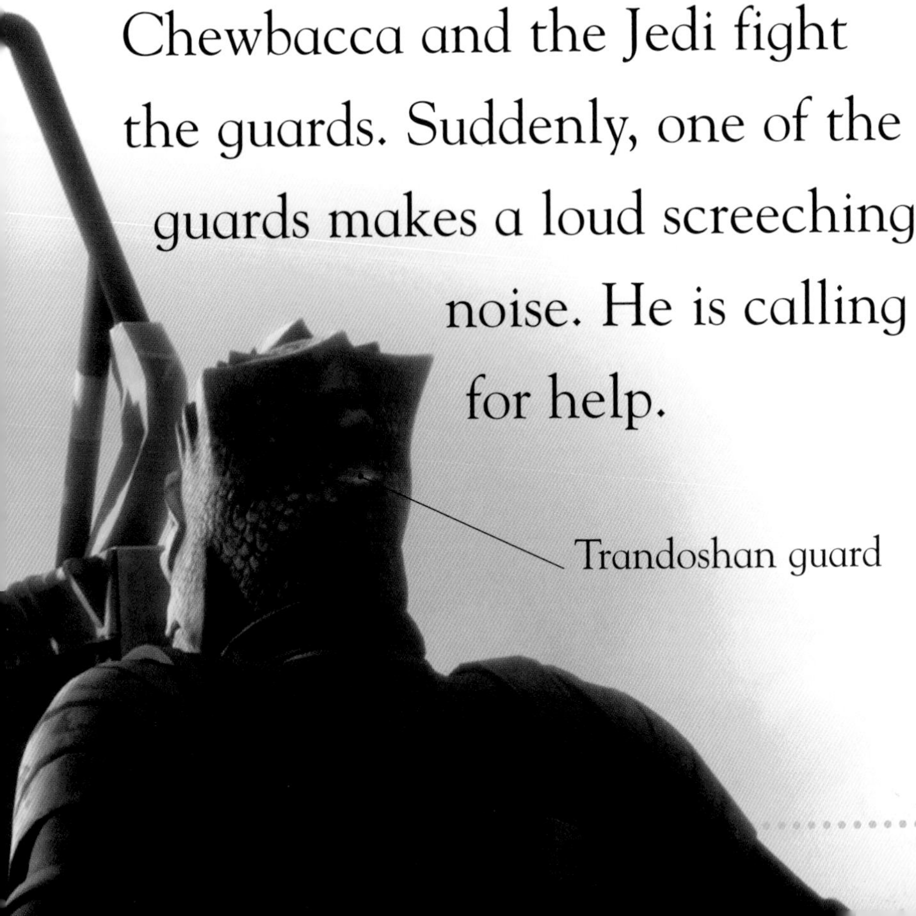

More Trandoshan guards arrive. They are armed with blasters. The Jedi use the Force to knock the guns out of their hands.

Chewbacca wrestles with one of the guards, while the Jedi fight the others.

More guards appear.
They overpower Chewbacca and the Jedi. Oh no!
The Trandoshans have defeated our heroes.

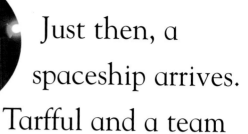

Just then, a spaceship arrives. Tarfful and a team of Wookiee warriors are on board. The transmitter did get a message to the Wookiees after all!

After a battle, Chewbacca and the Wookiee warriors finally defeat the Trandoshans.
At last, they can leave the moon!
Victory is theirs!

Future hero
We will see Chewbacca again. He will be a great Wookiee warrior in many battles during the Clone Wars and afterwards.

Quiz

1. What is the name of the Wookiee planet?
2. How long can Wookiees live?
3. What does Chewbacca try to fix on the crashed Trandoshan spaceship?
4. What is the name of Chewbacca's Wookiee best friend?

Put the scenes in the right order:

A

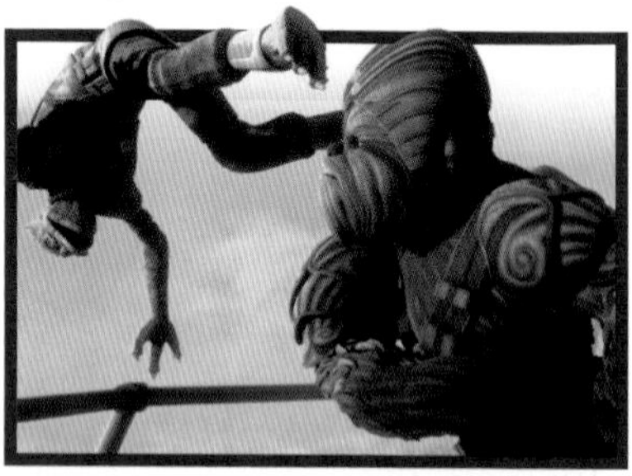

B

C

D

Answers: 1. Kashyyyk, 2. 600 years,
3. A transmitter, 4. Tarfful
The correct order is C, D, A, B